OUT FROM BONEVILLE

BY JEFF SMITH

WITH COLOR BY STEVE HAMAKER

An Imprint of

SCHOLASTIC

New York   Toronto   London   Auckland   Sydney   Mexico City   New Delhi   Hong Kong   Buenos Aires

This book is for Vijaya

Copyright © 2005 by Jeff Smith.

The chapters in this book were originally published in the comic book BONE and are copyright © 1991 and 1992 by Jeff Smith. BONE® is copyright © 2005 by Jeff Smith.

Library of Congress Cataloging-in-Publication Data is available.
ISBN-13: 978-0-439-70623-0 – ISBN-10: 0-439-70623-8 (hardcover)
ISBN 0-439-70640-8 (paperback)

ACKNOWLEDGMENTS
Harvestar Family Crest designed by Charles Vess
Map of *The Valley* by Mark Crilley

20 19 18 17 16 15   11 12
First Scholastic edition, February 2005
Book design by David Saylor
Printed in Singapore 46

CONTENTS

DON'T GET HIM STARTED.

THEY CAN'T **DO** THIS TO **ME!** YOU CAN'T DO ANYTHING TO A **RICH** PERSON THAT HE DOESN'T **WANT!**

GASP! OH! TH' HORRIBLE INJUSTICE OF IT ALL! I'M STILL REELING WITH SHOCK!!

I'M A RESPECTED COMMUNITY **LEADER!** A **SHINING PILLAR** OF **MORAL STRENGTH!**

...SO A COUPLE OF SHADY **BUSINESS** DEALS WENT SOUR... IS **THAT** ANY REASON TO RUN TH' MOST **BELOVED BONE** IN BONEVILLE OUT ON A **RAIL?!**

YES.

BELOVED? TH' MAYOR DECLARED A SCHOOL **HOLIDAY** JUST SO TH' KIDS COULD COME AND THROW **ROCKS** AT YOU!

INGRATES! OH, THEY'LL **RUE** TH' DAY THEY CHASED **PHONCIBLE P. BONE** OUTTA THEIR CRUMMY OL' TOWN!

SNIFF!

NOW, NOW, LITTLE BUCKAROO! DON'T BE **SAD!** IT'S A BEAUTIFUL DAY! THERE'S NOT A **CLOUD IN TH' SKY!**

THAT'S THE LAST STRAW!

DON'T GET MAD AT SMILEY BONE! THIS MESS ISN'T HIS FAULT!

THAT'S RIGHT! TH' TOWNSPEOPLE AREN'T MAD AT US! THEY RAN YOU OUTTA TOWN 'CAUSE YOU'RE A SELFISH, LITTLE GREEDBAG!

I CAN'T BELIEVE IT! NOT ONLY AM I BROKE - - NOW I'M GONNA DIE BROKE!

GASP! COFF! COFF!

OH, YOU'RE NOT GONNA DIE! I JUST HOPE YOU LEARNED YOUR LESSON!

WATER! I NEED WATER! I CAN FEEL MY TONGUE CRACKING!

HEY, COUSINS, LOOK WHAT I FOUND! I THINK IT'S A MAP!

?!

SURE ENOUGH! LOOK! IT'S A MAP OF THAT MOUNTAIN RANGE!

I'M SAVED! GIVE IT TO ME!

GIMME A DOLLAR FIRST.

WHAT?

GO ON, PHONEY! GIVE HIM A DOLLAR!

WHAT?!

WE'RE LOST IN THE MIDDLE OF TH' DESERT! GIVE HIM A DOLLAR!

YEEEE! I CAN'T **BELIEVE** I WASN'T JUST **KILLED!**

PHONEY! SMILEY! GO BACK! DON'T COME THIS WAY! IT'S A CLIFF!

...MAYBE THEY'RE ALREADY DOWN HERE!

PHONEY BONE! SMILEY!

HEY!

HEY, GUYS! I'M DOWN IN THIS GULLEY! CAN YOU HEAR ME?!!

HUH HUH HUH

HUFF!

WHERE TH' HECK **ARE** THOSE GUYS? WE'RE GOIN' STRAIGHT INTO TH' MOUNTAINS!

I HOPE I CATCH UP TO 'EM BEFORE IT GETS DARK . . . .

THE **LAST** THING I WANT TO DO IS SPEND THE NIGHT OUT HERE BY MYSELF!

. . . OF COURSE, AFTER A DAY LIKE **TODAY**, IT'S HARD TO IMAGINE THAT ANYTHING **WORSE** COULD HAPPEN . . .

YAWN!

OH, **MAN!** THIS AIN'T GONNA **CUT IT!**

I ACTUALLY THOUGHT THIS MAP WOULD TAKE ME THROUGH TH' MOUNTAINS TO THIS WATERFALL ON HERE . . .

. . . BUT IF THIS THING WERE **REAL**, I WOULD'VE COME TO TH' PASS BY **NOW!** **ERRR!** I'M SO **STUPID!** I BET THIS MAP WAS JUST ONE OF SMILEY'S **PRANKS** -- AND I **FELL** FOR IT!

AND TO TOP IT **OFF**, I HAVEN'T SEEN ANY MORE **CIGAR BUTTS** ALL DAY . . . **HOW** DO I GET MYSELF **INTO** THESE THINGS?

OH, WELL . . . I'LL FIND THOSE GUYS **SOONER** OR LATER . . . **IF** I DON'T DIE OF THIRST . . .

UNTIL **THEN,** I JUST GOTTA **KEEP MOVIN'!** KEEP . . .

COOL.

I MADE IT!

THAT STUPID MAP WAS **RIGHT!** YESSIREE, **BOB!** THERE'S WATER ON TH' MENU **TONIGHT!**

I COULD **KISS** SMILEY BONE FOR FINDING THAT MAP!

I MIGHT EVEN KISS **PHONEY** RIGHT BEFORE I STRANGLE HIM!

THE MAP

OUT FROM BONEVILLE

BUT YOU BETTER FIND IT - - **FAST!** IT'S AUTUMN NOW, AN' WINTER STRIKES **QUICK** IN THESE PARTS . . . AN' WHEN IT DOES, **NOBODY** CAN GET THROUGH THOSE MOUNTAINS . . .

. . . IN **OR** OUT!

SO I SUGGEST YOU MAKE YOUR VISIT HERE A **SHORT** ONE, OR YOU'LL BE STUCK FOR TH' WINTER. AN' I DON'T THINK YOU WANNA **DO** THAT!

NO. DEFINITELY NOT.

GOOD. I'LL LET YA GO FOR **NOW,** SINCE TED SEEMS TO LIKE YA OKAY... BUT DON'T FERGET!

NO DAWDLIN'!

THANK YOU FOR NOT HITTING ME.

DON'T WORRY 'BOUT HIM. . . HE'S ACTUAL A REAL NICE GUY!

WELL . . . NOW WE GOTTA FIGGER OUT WHAT TA **DO** WITH YA . . . SAY! I KNOW! I'LL TAKE YA TO SEE THORN! C'MON! WHAT'S YER **NAME,** MISTER?

FONE BONE. SO WHO'S THIS THORN? HE'S NOT ANOTHER **BIG BUG,** IS HE?

HO, HO! **NO!** THORN KNOWS JES' ABOUT EVER'THIN' IN TH' **WHOLE WORLD!**

BUT, LISTEN, BONE! BIG BROTHER WAS RIGHT ABOUT WINTER! SHE HITS **FAST!** 'N' IF YOU WANTS TA GIT HOME, YOU GOTTA DO IT BEFORE SHE **SNOWS!**

DON'T WORRY! I'M JUST GONNA FIND MY COUSINS, AN' THEN I'M **OUTTA HERE!**

TED! WAIT FOR ME!

WELL, WELL... LOOK WHO'S JOINED US FOR SUPPER... GO START THE COOKING FIRE!!

NO. YOU CALLED ME FAT.

NO?!! WHAT DO YOU MEAN NO?!!

AND IT'S NOT THE FIRST TIME YOU'VE DONE IT, EITHER...

COMRADE... BE REASONABLE! I WASN'T THINKING--- I WAS TRYING TO CATCH OUR DINNER --- THIS ISN'T THE TIME --

I TAKE IT BACK.... YOU'RE NOT FAT.

TOO LATE!

PLEASE, COMRADE! I JUST WANT TO CHOP HIM UP FOR THE STEW!

AND THAT'S ANOTHER THING! I'M TIRED OF STEW! I WANT TO PUT HIM IN A CRUST AND BAKE A LIGHT FLUFFY QUICHE!

QUICHE?! WHAT KIND OF FOOD IS THAT FOR A MONSTER TO EAT?!...... LISTEN, DO YOU THINK YOU COULD COME BACK IN HALF AN HOUR? WE'LL HAVE THIS STRAIGHTENED OUT BY THEN!

WHY DIDN'T YOU STOP ME?

WHY SHOULD I? YOU'RE SO SMART!

TED!

C'MON, TED! WHERE **ARE** YOU? YOU GOTTA TAKE ME TO SEE THORN!

- - I'M SORRY I CALLED YOU A **LEAF!**

WHOOOOOP! WATER! I HEAR **WATER!!**

WATER!

WATER! WATER!

WATER! MMMM **WATER!** WATER! MMMM WATER! WATER! MMMMMM MM MM OH. **MAN!**

WHAT AM I GONNA **DO?** WHAT IF I **CAN'T** FIND MY COUSINS BEFORE IT **SNOWS?** WE COULD BE **TRAPPED** HERE FOR TH' WHOLE **WINTER!**

I **GOTTA** GET OUTTA HERE! THIS FOREST IS TOO **WEIRD** FOR ME!

RUMMMBLE

HELLO, MIZ 'POSSUM! I HAVEN'T SEEN **YOU** IN A COUPLE OF MONTHS!

OH, I DON'T GET OUT OF TH' HOUSE MUCH IN **WINTER** 'SPECIALLY WITH **YOUNGUNS!**

THESE CAN'T BE **YOUR** KIDS! THEY'RE ALL GROWN UP!

WELL, IT'S ALMOST **SPRING!** THEY SHOOT UP **FAST** THIS TIME OF YEAR! YOU BOYS REMEMBER FONE BONE?

SURE!

YEAH!

HOW YOU GUYS DOIN'?

WE'RE COOL!

WHERE'D YA GET TH' **HAT?**

YOUR MOM MADE IT FOR ME!

PRETTY DORKY!

MOM BROUGHT YA SOME MORE **BLANKETS** 'N' STUFF!

WOW! THANKS! I DON'T KNOW **HOW** I WOULD'VE MADE IT THROUGH TH' WINTER WITHOUT YOU, MIZ 'POSSUM!

DON'T YOU **WORRY** ABOUT IT! AS LONG AS YOU'RE STUCK HERE IN OUR VALLEY, **I'LL** TAKE CARE OF YOU! **HERE!** I PACKED A PIE IN CASE YOU'RE HUNGRY!

DID YOU EVER FIND THOSE COUSINS OF YOURS?

NO, NOT YET. HAVE YOU SEEN **TED** SINCE I TALKED TO YOU LAST?

NOPE. DON'T KNOW MUCH ABOUT WHAT BUGS **DO** IN TH' WINTER, BUT I HAVEN'T SEEN WING **NOR** ANTENNAE OF TED SINCE TH' **SNOW** HIT...

SAY... WASN'T THERE SOMEONE **ELSE** YOU WANTED ME TO FIND OUT ABOUT?

TED WAS GONNA TAKE ME TO SEE SOMEONE NAMED **THORN.**

OH, THAT'S RIGHT! NOPE, HAVEN'T FOUND OUT A **THING!** YOU SURE YOU HAVE ENOUGH BLANKETS?

YES, MA'M. SIGH. WELL, THANKS ANYWAY, MIZ 'POSSUM.' IF THERE'S EVER ANYTHING I CAN **DO** --

AS A MATTER OF **FACT**, I'M ON MY WAY OVER TO MIZ HEDGEHOG'S PLACE, 'N' I WAS WONDERIN' IF YOU'D MIND WATCHIN' TH' KIDS?

ALL **RIGHT!** WE'RE GONNA STAY WITH FONE BONE!

ME?! BUT... **I** DON'T KNOW ANYTHING ABOUT BABY 'POSSUMS!'

IT'LL JUST BE FOR AN HOUR OR TWO! YOU BOYS BE **GOOD** NOW!

DON'T WORRY ABOUT **US**, MOM!

WELL... C'MON, GUYS. YOU CAN HELP ME PUT THE **FINISHING** TOUCH ON MY HOUSE!

RUN INSIDE WHERE IT'S WARM... I'LL JUST BE A SECOND!

WHOOP!

YIPPEE!

THERE WE GO! COZY AS AN IGLOO! BY THE TIME THIS MELTS, IT'LL BE **SPRING**, AN' THEN I'M **OUTTA** HERE!

SMASH! CRASH!

HEY, GUYS! TAKE IT **EASY** IN TH--

CRUNCH

WHAT TH' HECK WAS THAT?

HOLY COW!

WHAT ARE YOU TRYING TO **DO**?!! **KILL** EACH OTHER? C'MON, LET'S SIT BY THE FIREPLACE, AN' I'LL TELL YOU A STORY!

AW! WE WERE HAVIN' **FUN**!

WE DON'T **WANNA** HEAR A STORY!

WE WANNA **PLAY**!

HE CAN'T PLAY WITH US! HE DON'T KNOW **NUTHIN'** 'BOUT BABY 'POSSUMS! HE **SAID** SO!

PLAY WITH US, MR. BONE!

YEAH! C'MON!

WHAT DO YOU WANNA PLAY?

WHAT 'POSSUMS PLAY **BEST** IS PLAY "**DEAD**"!

LOOK OUT! IT'S A GIANT 'POSSUM-EATING BEAR!!

HMM.!

I KINDA **LIKE** THIS GAME.

HEH, HEH! LOOK AT 'EM! THEY LOOK LIKE LITTLE ANGELS! I GUESS BABYSITTING WON'T BE SO TOUGH **AFTER** ALL!

♪

HEE HEE HEE

HERE COMES THE **BEAR!** YOU BETTER WATCH OUT! I'M GONNA **EAT YOU UP!**

RRRRRRRRR!

WHEEE!

HA! HA!

RUN! TH' BEAR IS **CHASIN' US!**

HEY! STAY IN TH' HOUSE!

COME BACK HERE!

CATCH US IF YOU CAN!

HA! HA!

I'M **SERIOUS!** QUIT FOOLIN' AROUND!

BOYS?

ALL RIGHT.... THEY WANT ME TO CATCH 'EM ... I'LL **CATCH** 'EM!

AHA! HIDING IN TH' BUSHES ARE YOU ?!! WELL, MR. BEAR IS GETTING' **HUNGRY!!**

RRRRR-R-R! NOW I'M GOING TO---

WHoooooPS!

THOSE RAT CREATURES WOULD HAVE TO BE PRETTY STUPID TO FOLLOW ME ON TO THIS FRAIL, LITTLE BRANCH!

STUPID, STUPID RAT CREATURES!!

SNAP!

GASP!

OW!

UH ... WELL ... IT WAS NICE MEETING YOU, BUT I BETTER GO FIND TH' KIDS!

WHOA.

DON'T WORRY ABOUT THE KIDS. THEY'RE SAFE.

GO STRAIGHT DOWN THE HILL. IT'S A SHORTCUT TO MIZ 'POSSUM'S HOUSE.

...UH ... SURE!

THANKS!

!

HEY! HOW'D YOU KNOW I WAS LOOKING FOR MIZ 'POSSUM'S KIDS?!

BONE!

OH, YES! BY ALL **MEANS!** THERE'S A NICE, HOT **SPRING** JUST BACK OVER TH' HILL! WHY DON'T YOU STOP THERE TO FRESHEN UP! C'MON ALONG, BOYS! SAY THANK YOU TO UNCLE BONE!

THANK YOU!

DID HE REALLY SEE A DRAGON?

NOW, DEAR...

HMMF! DID **TOO** SEE A DRAGON!

WHAT DO THEY **THINK?** I LIT MY **HEAD** ON FIRE TO KEEP WARM?

...AN' HOW COME THAT DRAGON KNEW I WAS BABYSITTING TH' **'POSSUM** KIDS? WHAT'S HE DOIN'? **FOLLOWIN'** ME AROUND?

THIS PLACE IS **TOO** WEIRD! THE FIRST SIGN OF SPRING I SEE...**POW!** I'M TAKIN' OFF **RIGHT** THROUGH THOSE MOUNTAINS! WITH OR **WITHOUT** MY COUSINS!

SNAP!

UH, OH. WHAT WAS THAT?

♪ MMMMMM ♪

FOOM!

HELLO.

UM . . . ARE YOU **NEW** AROUND HERE?

FONE BONE! WHAT'S YOURS?!

PLEASED TO MEET YOU, FONE BONE! MY NAME IS THORN!

THORN. THAT'S **BEAUTIFUL!** THOR--

THORN?! YOU'RE THORN? DO YOU KNOW A LITTLE BUG NAMED **TED?!**

WHY, YES! I KNOW TED! HE'S A **VERY** GOOD FRIEND OF MINE!

HOTCHA! THIS IS **GREAT!**

I'VE BEEN LOOKIN' FOR YOU **ALL WINTER!!**

YOU HAVE? WHY?

TED! HE TOLD ME TO FIND YOU! HE SAID THAT YOU KNOW **EVERYTHING!**

WELL, THAT CERTAINLY **SOUNDS** LIKE TED.

GREAT! THEN YOU CAN HELP ME AND MY COUSINS GET BACK TO **BONEVILLE?**

COUSINS? YOU MEAN THERE'S **MORE** OF YOU?

YEAH! THEY'RE STUCK IN THIS VALLEY, TOO! BUT I HAVEN'T SEEN EITHER ONE OF 'EM SINCE WE GOT HIT BY THAT SWARM OF **LOCUSTS!**

YOU DON'T SAY.

Y'KNOW. . . I **SHOULD'VE** ASKED THAT **DRAGON** IF **HE'D** SEEN MY COUSINS!

YOU SHOULD'VE ASKED **WHO**?

THE **DRAGON**! OH ... WAIT A MINUTE! **I** GET IT! YOU DON'T BELIEVE IN DRAGONS, **DO** YOU?

NO. SHOULD I?

NEVER MIND! I DON'T **CARE**!

ONCE I'M BACK IN **BONEVILLE**, I'LL NEVER EVEN HAVE TO **THINK** ABOUT DRAGONS OR THIS CRAZY VALLEY **AGAIN**!

WELL, I'D **LIKE** TO HELP...

WELL, C'MON! THERE'S NO TIME TO LOSE!!

...**BUT**...

I'VE NEVER **HEARD** OF BONEVILLE.

THERE **IS** A LITTLE VILLAGE DOWN THE ROAD CALLED BARRELHAVEN... DOES THAT HELP?

...WHAT'S WRONG?

NOTHIN'

FONE BONE?

OH... I DON'T BELONG IN THIS FOREST. MY HOME'S ON THE OTHER SIDE OF THE MOUNTAINS...

I'M SURE WE CAN GET YOU THROUGH THE MOUNTAINS AS SOON AS THE SNOW MELTS!

IT'S NOT JUST THAT! EVEN IF I **COULD** GET THROUGH THE MOUNTAINS, I'D **NEVER** FIND MY WAY BACK ACROSS THE DESERT. YOU WERE MY LAST HOPE.

WELL, LET'S JUST CONCENTRATE ON FINDING YOUR COUSINS. YOU'RE **SURE** THEY'RE HERE IN THE VALLEY?

PRETTY SURE, UNLESS THE RAT CREATURES GOT 'EM.

DID YOU SAY **RAT CREATURES?**

LET ME GUESS... YOU DON'T **BELIEVE** IN RAT CREATURES.

OH, YES I **DO!** HAVE YOU SEEN ONE **RECENTLY?**

I SAW **TWO** OF 'EM! TH' DRAGON CHASED 'EM OFF!

NOW LISTEN TO ME... THIS IS IMPORTANT! YOU'RE NOT FOOLING AROUND? YOU **REALLY** SAW TWO RAT CREATURES?

YEAH! I REALLY SAW A **DRAGON,** TOO! LOOK AT MY **HEAD!** WHAT DO YOU THINK **THIS** IS? A **TAN?!**

MY! YOU MUST'VE **ENJOYED** YOUR FIRST NIGHT IN A HOUSE AFTER SLEEPING IN THE **WOODS**! YOU DIDN'T EVEN **HEAR** ME WHEN I CAME DOWNSTAIRS!

CAKES?

HERE'S YOUR CAKES! AND HERE'S SOME TEA!

THENK YOU.

HELLO? ARE YOU **AWAKE** YET, FONE BONE? IT'S **ME**, THORN!

THORN?

AH! **YOU'RE** AWAKE! GOOD! NOW EAT YOUR BREAKFAST! WE'VE GOT A LOT TO **DO** TODAY! GRAN'MA BEN IS COMING HOME FROM THE VILLAGE, AND I WANT TO CLEAN THE PLACE UP BEFORE SHE GETS HERE!

SHE'S COMING HOME **TODAY?**

THAT'S **RIGHT!** SHE GOES INTO **BARRELHAVEN** EVERY SPRING TO SHOW OFF HER BEST **RACING** COWS!

YOUR GRAN'MA RACES **COWS?!**

YEAH! SHE'S PRETTY **GOOD**, TOO! THERE'S HARDLY A COW IN THE WHOLE **VALLEY** THAT CAN BEAT HER IN A **100-YARD DASH!**

HUH! I'M **DEFINITELY** LOOKING FORWARD TO **MEETING** THIS LADY!

OH, IT'S A **BIG EVENT** HERE IN THE SPRING! PEOPLE BET **CHICKENS** AND **GOATS** -- SOME FOLKS BET THEIR WHOLE LIVESTOCK ON HER! IF YOU WANT TO MAKE A GOOD IMPRESSION, BE SURE TO COMPLIMENT HER ON HER **COWS!** SHE'S **REAL** PROUD OF HER COWS!

I'LL TRY TO REMEMBER THAT.

NOW, IF YOU'RE DONE EATING, WHY DON'T WE GO GET SOME WATER?

OKAY BY ME! LET'S **DO IT!**

HOW ABOUT IF WE GET THE FIREWOOD **LATER?**

SIGH.

SO ... DO YOU THINK YOUR GRAN'MA WILL MIND ME **STAYIN'** WITH YOU GUYS? I MEAN-- I DON'T WANNA CAUSE ANY PROBLEMS!

SHE WON'T MIND! SHE WOULDN'T MAKE YOU GO BACK OUT IN THE **WOODS** -- ESPECIALLY WITH THOSE **RAT CREATURES** AROUND!

I HOPE NOT.

JUST DO ME ONE FAVOR! WHEN GRAN'MA BEN GETS HERE, **TRY** NOT TO MENTION YOUR FRIEND THE **DRAGON!**

WHY NOT?

BECAUSE DRAGONS DON'T **EXIST**, THAT'S WHY!

WHAT DO YOU **MEAN?** YOU BELIEVE IN **RAT CREATURES!** WHY DON'T YOU BELIEVE IN **DRAGONS?**

BECAUSE **EVERYBODY** BELIEVES IN RAT CREATURES! BUT **YOU'RE** THE ONLY ONE WHO'S EVER SEEN A **DRAGON!**

I DON'T BELIEVE IT!

YOU **HAVEN'T**? YOU MUST'VE HAD A DEPRIVED CHILDHOOD. **THESE** I BROUGHT FOR PHONEY BONE . . . THEY'RE **FINANCIAL MAGAZINES!**

DIDN'T YOU BRING ANYTHING FOR YOURSELF?

SURE! THIS IS **MOBY DICK!** IT'S MY **FAVORITE BOOK!** I'VE READ IT **THREE TIMES!**

WHAT'S IT ABOUT?

UH . . . ARE YOU **SURE** YOU WANT TO KNOW? EVERY TIME I TRY TO TELL PEOPLE ABOUT MOBY DICK THEIR **EYES** GLAZE OVER!

TRY ME.

OKAY! IT'S ABOUT A WHALING VOYAGE, AN' THIS GUY **ISHMAEL** ----

Z

HA. HA. **VERY** FUNNY.

WHAT ELSE HAVE YOU GOT IN HERE?

LET'S SEE . . . A BLANKET . . . AN OLD MAP THAT SMILEY FOUND . . . . . .

THAT'S ABOUT **IT!** THE ONE THING I DIDN'T BRING ENOUGH OF WAS **FOOD** AND **WATER!** WELL, TH' **TWO** THINGS ....

WHY ARE YOU MAKING THAT FACE?

I DON'T KNOW .... SOMETHING ABOUT THIS MAP IS FAMILIAR ...

REALLY? SMILEY FOUND IT OUT IN TH' DESERT RIGHT BEFORE WE GOT SPLIT UP.

IT REMINDS ME OF A DREAM I USED TO HAVE ...

WHOA. AND YOU THINK **MY** STORIES ARE STRANGE!

ARE YOU OKAY?

I'M FINE, LET'S JUST FORGET IT. C'MON, GRAN'MA WILL BE HERE SOON ...

SLURK GUKK BURRRRP!

SIGH.

WHAT A **TRAVESTY!** TH' MOST **CHERISHED** AND **RESPECTED** (NOT TO MENTION WEALTHIEST!) BONE IN BONEVILLE-- OUT IN TH' WOODS-- FENDING OFF TH' ELEMENTS WITH HIS BARE HANDS!

FORCED TO **EKE** OUT A MISERABLE EXISTENCE **AMIDST TH' ROCKS 'N' MUD!!**

OH, CRUEL, CRUEL, FATE! WHY HAVE YOU ABANDONED YOUR MOST BELOVED SON?!

GOD, I PITY ME.

HEY, YOU! WAKE UP!

MM?

THE NAME'S PHONEY BONE... TH' **RICHEST** BONE IN BONEVILLE! YOU'VE PROBABLY **HEARD** OF ME! I'M LOOKIN' FOR A GUY NAMED FONE BONE. YOU SEEN HIM?

HEY! LET'S KICK THAT PEA-SIZED **DINOSAUR BRAIN** INTO HIGH GEAR, HUH?

WOULD IT HELP IF I ASKED TH' QUESTION AGAIN **SLOWER**?

HAVE......YOU.....

...SEEN FONE BONE..... .....A-**ROUND**?

UH, HEY, THERE, MISTER! MAYBE YOU BETTER LET **ME** HELP YOU!

MAYBE I **BETTER!** IT COULD BE **DAYS** BEFORE TH' MESSAGE REACHES **THIS** GUY'S BRAIN!

HOW 'BOUT WE TAKE A FEW STEPS OFF TO STARBOARD... OUTTA **FIRIN' RANGE** ... AN' **I'LL** ANSWER YER QUESTIONS FOR YA.

OH, YEAH? AN' WHO ARE YOU?

I'M TED! I'M A BUG!

SPARE ME TH' **DETAILS,** FRIEND! I'M LOOKIN' FOR A GUY NAMED FONE BONE. YOU **SEEN** HIM?

BONE? OH, YEAH.' I SEEN HIM.'

YOU **HAVE?!** I'M **SAVED!** WHERE IS HE?

DON'T KNOW. AIN'T SEEN HIM SINCE BEFORE SHE **SNOWED.**

HA! A **LIKELY** STORY! BUG! TAKE ME TO YOUR **LEADER!**

TAKE YOU TO MY LEADER?

C'MON! C'MON! I AIN'T GOT ALL DAY!

WHO SHOULD I TAKES YA TO?

I NEED **ANSWERS,** BUG! I DEMAND **SATISFACTION!**

I GUESS I COULD TAKE YA TO SEE THORN'S GRAN'MA ...

FINE. FINE. WHAT- EVER!

BUT I GOTS TA WARN YA ... SHE'S A **OL'** LADY, AN' SHE MIGHT NOT TAKE TO YER ATTITUDE MUCH ...

DON'T WORRY ABOUT **ME,** BUG! THERE AIN'T A WOMAN **ALIVE** WHO CAN RESIST MY CHARMS!

OKEE DOKEE... I WAS JES WARNIN' YA, THAT'S ALL.

WELL, MOVE IT OUT, BUG! THIS IS TAKING **FOREVER** ON THOSE LITTLE LEGS OF YOURS!

OKEE DOKEE...

HI, GRAN'MA! HOW YOU **DOIN'**?

WELL, HELLO, TED, DEAR!

GRAN'MA, THIS HERE FELLA BEEN ASKIN' TA MEET YA!

OH, HE LOOKS LIKE SUCH A **NICE** YOUNG MAN. WOULD HE LIKE TO RIDE ONE OF MY RACING COWS?

NO, I DON'T WANNA RIDE ONE OF YER **STUPID COWS!**

TED, DEAR, I THINK YOU'D BETTER LEAVE. I'M GONNA TEAR THIS LITTLE FELLA APART FROM THE INSIDE **OUT**.

YES, MA'M. (SEE YA AROUND, PAL.)

DO YOU LIKE APPLE PIE, FONE BONE?

LIKE IT? IT'S MY FAVORITE **HOBBY!**

WELL, DON'T GET **TOO** EXCITED!

THIS IS FOR **GRAN'MA** -- SHE **LOVES** MY SPECIAL APPLE PIE...

...AND WE WANT TO BE **REAL** NICE TO GRAN'MA BEFORE WE ASK ABOUT YOU **STAYING HERE!**

CLINK CLINK

HEY! WHAT'S GOIN' ON?! TH' WHOLE CABIN'S STARTIN' TO SHAKE!

IT'S GRAN'MA! SHE'S HOME!

YOUR GRAN'MA?! IT SOUNDS LIKE A STAMPEDE!

THAT'S HER! SHE MUST BE RACING ONE OF THE COWS!

LOOK OUTSIDE! THAT'S HER FASTEST COW COMING ACROSS THE CLEARING!

NO WAY!

AND HERE COMES GRAN'MA! C'MON, GRAN'MA!

SHE'S GONNA OUTRUN THAT COW?! SHE'LL HAVE A HEART ATTACK!

HEY! DO YOU SEE THAT? THERE'S SOMETHING ON THE COW.

WHAT? WHERE?

--THERE'S SOMEONE RIDING THE COW!

OH, MY GOD! IT'S PHONEY BONE!

WHAT HAPPENED TO **PHONEY**?

-- UH, OH --

I **THINK** HE'S IN THE **FIREPLACE**!

I'M COMIN' PHONEY!

HURRY, GRAN'MA! HE'S **STUCK** IN THE FIREPLACE!

OH, MY GOODNESS! HE'LL RUIN TH' DINNER!

HANG ON! I'LL GET YOU OUT!

FONE BONE! SAVE ME! THAT CRAZY OLD LADY TRIED TO KILL ME!!

WELL, BLESS MY **BUTTONS**! WHAT HAVE WE GOT HERE?

WATCH OUT! DON'T LET HER GET AHOLD OF YOU!

H-- H'LO, MA'M!

DO **YOU** LIKE COWS? I KNOW YOUR **FRIEND** DOESN'T.

I DON'T LIKE TO **RIDE** 'EM, YOU OL' BAT!

FONE BONE **LOVES** COWS!

SORRY, DEAR. YOU CAN'T KEEP HIM.

BUT--

NO BUTS. I DON'T WANT ANY PETS RUNNING AROUND TH' HOUSE.

GRAN'MA! THEY'RE NOT **PETS!**

CAN YOU **MILK** 'EM? IF YOU CAN'T **MILK** 'EM, THEY'RE **PETS!**

THAT'S IT! I'M OUTTA HERE!

GRAN'MA!

SAY... IS THAT **APPLE PIE** I SMELL?

YES! I BAKED ONE OF MY **SPECIAL** PIES JUST FOR YOU!

WHAT A SWEET THING YOU ARE!

QUICK! WHILE SHE'S DISTRACTED!

HOLD IT! THORN THINKS GRAN'MA BEN CAN HELP US GET BACK TO BONEVILLE!

IT'S NOT WORTH IT! LET GO OF ME!

WOULD YOU **WAIT** A MINUTE?!! WE CAN **EXPLAIN** EVERYTHING!

HELP! HELP! THEY'VE **DESTROYED** MY COUSIN'S **BRAIN!!** OH, MY GOD! THEY'VE ALREADY **MILKED** YOU, HAVEN'T THEY?!!

GRAN'MA, THEY'RE **BONES**! THEY COME FROM A PLACE CALLED BONEVILLE! AND THEY NEED OUR HELP TO GET **BACK**!

WHERE'S SMILEY?

SMILEY? I THOUGHT HE WAS WITH **YOU**!

YOU HAVEN'T SEEN HIM SINCE WE SPLIT UP? BUT I **KNOW** HE'S IN TH' VALLEY! I FOUND ONE OF HIS **CIGAR BUTTS**!

TH' LAST TIME I SAW THAT CHOWDERHEAD, HE WAS SAYIN' HOW **COOL** IT WAS THAT WE WERE ABOUT TO BE PULVERIZED BY INSECTS!

YEAH! THAT'S TH' LAST TIME **I** SAW HIM, TOO. . .

AW, QUIT YER **WORRYIN'**! WHY DON'T YA INTRODUCE ME TO YER **GOOD-LOOKIN'** FRIEND, HERE?

OH! UH. . . PHONEY, THIS IS THORN! THORN, PHONEY.

SO, WHAT'VE YOU BEEN DOIN' WITH MY COUSIN? YOU TWO GOT A LITTLE **THING** GOIN', OR WHAT?

PHONEY!

NO, HUH? FIGURES! WHAT'D YA **DO**? BORE HER TO DEATH TALKIN' ABOUT **MOBY DICK**?

I'M GOING TO BED. YOU CAN KEEP 'EM IF YOU WANT, BUT THEY HAVE TO SLEEP IN TH' BARN.

GRAM!

G'NIGHT MA'M IT WAS NICE MEETING YOU!

FONE BONE, COULD I TALK TO YOU FOR A MOMENT? OUTSIDE?

YES.

WELL, GO AHEAD! I AIN'T STOPPIN' YA!

THIS ISN'T GOING QUITE THE WAY WE PLANNED, IS IT? TELL ME. . . IS HE ALWAYS LIKE THIS?

PRETTY MUCH.

HMM. GRAN'MA'S GOING BACK TO BARRELHAVEN IN A FEW DAYS FOR THE SPRING FESTIVAL. IF WE CAN JUST KEEP THOSE TWO CALM UNTIL THEN, WE CAN ALL GO INTO TOWN TOGETHER TO LOOK FOR YOUR OTHER COUSIN.

DON'T WORRY! I CAN HANDLE PHONEY!

GO BACK IN THE HOUSE AND KEEP AN EYE ON HIM. I HAVE TO GO GET SOME FRESH WATER FOR GRAN'MA TO WASH UP WITH . . .

OKAY, PHONEY! WE HAVE TO GET A COUPLE OF THINGS STRAIGHT---

COME ON! A LITTLE HONEST WORK ISN'T GOING TO KILL YOU!

A **LITTLE**?! THAT CRAZY OL' LADY IS RUNNIN' OUR **BUTTS** OFF! MILK TH' COWS! **FEED** TH' COWS! TAKE CARE OF TH' **CHICKENS!**

GRAN'MA BEN IS **FEEDING** US **AND** LETTIN' US STAY IN HER BARN! TH' **LEAST** WE CAN DO IS HELP OUT!

TH' BARN **STINKS**, AND IT'S **DRAFTY**! IF IT WASN'T FOR TH' **FOOD**, I'D RATHER TAKE MY CHANCES BACK OUT IN TH' **WOODS!**

WE'RE GONNA **END UP** IN TH' WOODS IF YOU DON'T CLEAN THIS UP AN' GET ANOTHER BUCKET OF **MILK!**

I SHOULD'VE **KNOWN** YOU WOULDN'T UNDERSTAND! YOU NEVER HAD ANY **REAL** MONEY! YOU DON'T KNOW WHAT IT'S **LIKE** TO LOSE EVERYTHING! **YOU** DON'T KNOW WHAT IT'S LIKE TO BE **BROKE!**

I'M **HERE**, AREN'T I? BESIDES, YOU'RE NOT **BROKE**! YOU'VE STILL GOT A WAD OF BILLS ON YOU!

ONLY A COUPLE OF THOUSAND. . . STILL, THEY **DO** GIVE ME **SOME** COMFORT! LOOK! AREN'T THEY BEAUTIFUL?

AAAAH!

THEY'RE GETTING **WRINKLED**! I'M TELLIN' YA, FONE BONE, I CAN'T **TAKE** MUCH MORE OF THIS!!

IT'S NOT FOR MUCH **LONGER**! AS SOON AS WE FIND SMILEY BONE WE'RE GONNA GET OUTTA HERE! UNTIL **THEN**, JUST **TRY** NOT TO GET US KICKED OFF TH' FARM, OKAY?

ALL RIGHT, ALL RIGHT. COOL YER JETS! I'LL TRY NOT TO CAUSE ANY TROUBLE.

GOOD! I'VE GOTTA GO FIND **THORN** . . . I PROMISED I'D HELP HER CHURN BUTTER TODAY!

YEAH, YEAH. STICK SOME HAY IN MY TEETH AN' CALL ME GOOBER!

CHEER UP, PHONEY! BREAKFAST WILL BE READY SOON!

RRRRR.

MORNIN', BONE!

GOOD MORNIN', GRAN'MA! YOU ALL SET FOR OUR BIG TRIP TO **BARRELHAVEN** TOMORROW?

I'M STILL **PACKIN'**-- I SEEM TO BE MISSING A PAIR OF **BLOOMERS**, THOUGH . . . YOU AN' YOUR COUSIN WOULDN'T KNOW ANYTHING ABOUT THAT, WOULD YOU?

NO, MA'M!

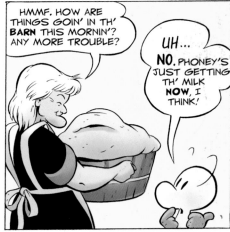

HMMF. HOW ARE THINGS GOIN' IN TH' **BARN** THIS MORNIN'? ANY MORE TROUBLE?

UH... **NO.** PHONEY'S JUST GETTING TH' MILK **NOW**, I THINK!

THAT'S GOOD. WE'VE GOT A TIGHT SCHEDULE----

YES, MA'M! THORN AND I ARE GOING TO CHURN BUTTER, AND BAKE THESE LITTLE BREAD THINGS WITH STUFF IN 'EM TO TAKE ON TH' JOURNEY-

OH, NO . . . .

WHAT?

DON'T YOU WANT TH' BREAD THINGS?

IT'S NOT TH' **BREAD**, BONE! IT'S TH' **GITCHY FEELIN'**! - - IT JUST COME **AT** ME OUTTA TH' **BLUE!**

TH' GITCHY FEELIN'? WHAT'S THAT?

TH' **GITCHY!** IT'S A **TERRIBLE** FEELIN' THAT MAKES YOUR HEAD **SWIM**, AN' YOUR LEGS **WOBBLE!** IT'S A POWERFUL **OMEN** OF BAD **THINGS** TO **COME!**

...THERE . . . IT'S STARTIN' TO PASS. MAYBE WHATEVER'S GOIN' TO HAPPEN WON'T BE SO BAD...

ARE YOU OKAY?

IT'S GONE NOW. BUT TH' GITCHY FEELIN' IS **NEVER** WRONG! YOU KEEP AN EYE ON THAT COUSIN OF YOURS, YOU HEAR?

YES MA'M!

YOU **NEVER** LEARN, DO YOU?

I **SHOULDA** STUCK WITH MY FIRST IDEA!

WHAT? COMBINING A **SLAUGHTERHOUSE** WITH A **PETTING ZOO?!** OH, YEAH! **THAT** WAS **BRILLIANT!**

AHH! WHAT DO **YOU** KNOW?

CAN'T YOU MAKE IT THROUGH **ONE MORE DAY** WITHOUT GETTING US IN **TROUBLE?** WE'RE GOIN' INTO TOWN WITH GRAN'MA **TOMORROW!**

WHAT ARE WE WAITIN' FOR **HER** FOR? LET'S BLOW THIS POPSICLE STAND **NOW!**

TOMORROW IS TH' FIRST DAY OF TH' **SPRING FAIR!** THIS'LL BE OUR **BEST SHOT** AT FINDING SMILEY BONE!

GRAN'MA SAID THAT **LAST** WEEK PEOPLE WERE ALREADY COMIN' IN FROM **ALL OVER** TH' VALLEY- - - SETTIN' UP **BOOTHS** AN' GETTIN' **READY!**

WELL, **I** FIGURE -- IF SMILEY'S SOMEWHERE IN TH' VALLEY, HE'S **BOUND** TO HAVE HEARD ABOUT GRAN'MA'S **COW RACE!** YOU **KNOW** HOW MUCH HE LIKES TO BET ON **RACES!**

HO -- BACK UP! YOU MEAN PEOPLE ACTUALLY BET **MONEY** ON THAT OL' BAG TO BEAT A **COW** IN A **FOOTRACE?**

I **KNOW!** IT'S **CRAZY,** BUT THORN SAYS IT'S A BIG DEAL HERE! SOME FOLKS BET EVERYTHING THEY'VE **GOT!**

OKAY, FONE BONE! **I'LL** BE GOOD! I POSITIVELY **GUARANTEE** YOU WON'T HEAR ANOTHER **PEEP** OUTTA ME ALL DAY!

REALLY?

YEAH, NOW GET OFF MY BACK! GO CHURN SOME BUTTER WITH THORN! I'VE GOT STUFF TO DO!

WHAT? WHAT ARE YOU UP TO?

NOTHING! I SAID I WON'T MESS UP YOUR PLAN TO GO INTO TOWN TO LOOK FOR SMILEY, AN' I **MEANT** IT!

AND I WON'T HEAR A **PEEP** OUTTA YOU TH' REST OF TH' **DAY**, RIGHT?

RIGHT! JEEZ! DO YA WANT IT IN **WRITING?!**

DO YOU HAVE A PIECE OF PAPER?

I THINK I HEAR THORN CALLIN' YA.

REALLY?! OKAY, PHONEY! SEE YA TONIGHT!

YEP, YOU WON'T HEAR A **PEEP** OUTTA **ME**, 'CAUSE **I** AIN'T GONNA **BE** HERE!

FONE BONE WON'T MIND IF I BORROW A FEW OF HIS THINGS... I MIGHT NEED 'EM ON MY WAY TO TOWN...

SOUNDS LIKE A LOTTA **MONEY'S** GONNA CHANGE HANDS TOMORROW, AN' I DON'T SEE WHY GRAN'MA BEN SHOULD **HOG** IT ALL!

NO, SIRREE! IF THERE'S **BOOKMAKIN'** TO BE DONE, **I'M** TH' MAN TO **DO** IT!

HEY, THORN! WHERE WE GOIN'?

DOWN TO THE SPRINGS!

OH, FONE BONE, YOU'RE GOING TO **LOVE** THE FESTIVAL! WE'LL SEE JUGGLERS, AND TUMBLERS, AND SINGERS! AND MY **FAVORITE** PART-- THE **BOOTHS!**

THERE ARE **ROWS** AND **ROWS** OF **BOOTHS**, AND YOU CAN BUY THE MOST **AMAZING** THINGS! THEY HAVE **HONEY**, AND **PEACOCK FEATHERS**, AND **SILK ROBES!**

I USUALLY ONLY GET TO LOOK-- BUT **THIS** YEAR I'M GOING TO GET A BOTTLE OF **DYE** FROM THE SOUTH, AND I'M GOING TO MAKE A BEAUTIFUL **BLUE DRESS!**

HOW COME WE DIDN'T BRING ANY BUCKETS TO CARRY TH' WATER BACK IN?

WE'RE NOT GETTING WATER. WE'RE TAKING A BATH!

A BATH? WHAT **KIND** OF BATH?

OHMYGOSH

YOU WANT TO GET CLEANED UP FOR THE FESTIVAL, DON'T YOU? C'MON!

CRACK

CRUNCH

SNAP

RRRR. THERE WAS A **PATH** HERE A **SECOND** AGO! WHAT HAPPENED TO IT?

WHY DOESN'T SOMEBODY BUILD SOME **ROADS** IN THIS PLACE?!

HMM. MAYBE I SHOULD LOOK INTO THAT. . . .

I COULD BUILD A **TOLL ROAD!**

YEAH! I CAN ALMOST **HEAR** THOSE LITTLE COINS CALLING OUT TO ME **NOW--**

HELLO, BONE!

OVER HERE! IN TH' TREE!

WHAT ARE YOU KIDS DOIN' HANGIN' AROUND HERE? GET A JOB!

SORRY, MISTER! WE THOUGHT YOU WERE SOMEONE ELSE!

WE THOUGHT YOU WERE FONE BONE!

I'M HIS COUSIN.

HIS **COUSIN**? ALL **RIGHT!** YOU WANNA PLAY WITH US?

WE'RE LEARNIN' HOW TO HANG BY OUR TAILS!

NO, THANKS. I'M ON MY WAY INTO TOWN.

HEY, MISTER! YOU KNOW TH' **WAY** INTO TOWN?

YEAH. WHY?

IT'S **THAT** WAY.

OH! RIGHT!

THANKS, KID! WHEN I COME BACK, I'LL BRING YOU A **CARROT!**

A CARROT? WHAT'S HE THINK WE ARE? RABBITS?

WHAT A DORK.

LUCKY THING I RAN INTO THOSE KIDS! AS SOON AS I'M BACK ON TH' RIGHT PATH, I SHOULD GET TO BARRELHAVEN IN **NO TIME!**

TH' FIRST THING I GOTTA DO IS HIT TH' LOCAL TAVERN, AN' FIND OUT WHO'S IN TOWN TO BET ON TH' RACE . . .

SNIFF

SNIff! SNiff! OOOH! MAN! SOMETHING AROUND HERE SURE **STINKS!**

JEEZ! IT'S GETTIN' **WORSE!**

WHOA.

WHAT TH' **HECK** ARE **THOSE** THINGS?

UH, OH! SOMEBODY'S COMIN'!

GET UP, YOU TWO.

ZZRT SNORT! WHA--?

EVERYTHING'S READY FOR TOMORROW. I JUST WISH I COULD SHAKE THIS **GITCHY** FEELIN' I GOT!

DID YOU FIND TH' LITTLE SQUIRT?

NO. AN' MY **BOOTS** AN' **KNAPSACK** ARE MISSING, TOO! I THINK HE WENT INTO TOWN WITHOUT US!

WE LOOKED FOR HIM, BUT THERE'S NO SIGN OF HIM ON THE ROAD. WE WENT ALL THE WAY TO OLD MAN'S CAVE BEFORE IT GOT TOO DARK. I'M SURE WE'LL FIND HIM AT THE FAIR TOMORROW.

HMM. I DON'T LIKE IT. AN' THERE'S A BAD MOON OUT TONIGHT, TOO.

RUN BACK TO TH' BARN, AN' GET YOUR BLANKET. I THINK YOU BETTER COME IN TH' HOUSE WITH US TONIGHT.

OKAY.

.... APPROACH ME....

....I HAVE RECEIVED WORD THAT THE ONE WE SEEK HAS BEEN SEEN IN YOUR TERRITORY.... ...HOW IS IT THAT YOU HAVE NOT BROUGHT HIM TO ME?

WE -- WE HAVE NOT SEEN THE ONE WHO BEARS THE STAR--

BUT ON SEVERAL OCCASIONS WE HAVE SEEN ONE WHO IS MUCH LIKE HIM IN DESCRIPTION.... HE IS CALLED FONE BONE....

WE FIRST SAW HIM ON THE WESTERN RIDGE -- ON THE DRAGONS' STAIR-- WE HAVE SEEN THIS NEW CREATURE TWICE MORE IN THE VALLEY NEAR THE WATERFALL....

DID YOU THINK THIS WAS INSIGNIFICANT? WHY DID YOU NOT CAPTURE THE CREATURE AND BRING IT TO THE COUNCIL?

...HE BEARS NO STAR...

WE TRIED TO CAPTURE HIM, MASTER....BUT HE IS CHARMED! HE IS UNDER THE PROTECTION OF THE GREAT RED DRAGON!

WE TRIED TO SPY.... BUT THE DRAGON TREADS A WIDE CIRCLE AROUND HIM...

THE CREATURE IS ON A SMALL FARM NEAR THE HOT SPRINGS... HE STAYS WITH THE OLD COW WOMAN ...MOTHER BEN.....

...., THESE ARE GRAVE TIDINGS....IT WOULD NOT BE WELL FOR THE DRAGON TO LEARN OF OUR PLANS....

....IF WE MUST RISK A CONFRONTATION..... WE MUST DO IT NOW... WHILE THE DRAGON'S SUSPICIONS SLEEP....

KINGDOK...PREPARE TWO WAR PARTIES.....TAKE A THOUSAND WARRIORS IN EACH....

WITH THE FIRST.... SCOUR THE COUNTRYSIDE... SEARCH THE ROAD AND THE LANDS BEYOND THE WATERFALL.... FIND THE ONE WHO BEARS THE STAR.....

....IF THE DRAGON IS STILL WATCHING....THIS ACTIVITY WILL DRAW HIM OFF...LEAVING THE OLD COW WOMAN UNGUARDED.....

SEND THE SECOND PARTY TO THE FARMHOUSE..... ...DESTROY IT....... ...KILL THE NEW CREATURE...

LET US HOPE THAT THE DEATH OF THIS FONE BONE WILL CAUSE THE DRAGON TO LEAVE THE VALLEY AND RETURN TO DEREN GARD....

...GO NOW.... WE ATTACK TONIGHT!

GET UP! GET UP!

CREEEAK

SO I'VE HEARD!

IS ANYBODY DOIN' TH' **BOOKMAKIN'**?

NOT YET... BUT FROM WHAT I'VE PICKED UP-- YOUR FRIEND **GRAN'MA** IS TH' **ODDS-ON** FAVORITE!

GREAT! PERFECT! HOW MUCH TIME DO WE HAVE?

ONE WEEK.

EXCELLENT! I GOT AN **IDEA** THAT'LL MAKE US A **LOTTA** MONEY!

UH, OH! I HOPE THIS ISN'T GONNA BE ONE OF THOSE **SILLY** IDEAS YOU USED TO PULL BACK IN **BONEVILLE!**

WHAT?! WHAT ARE YOU **TALKIN'** ABOUT? **WHAT** SILLY IDEAS?!

REMEMBER TH' **FIRST** TIME YOU GOT US RUN OUT OF TOWN? YOU OPENED UP A CHAIN OF FRANCHISES -- **BONE ENVIRONMENTAL**: NUCLEAR REACTOR AND ENDLESS SALAD BARS!

THAT WASN'T A **SILLY** IDEA! TH' **LETTUCE** WOULDN'T SPOIL FOR **DECADES!**

WELL, IT WAS **PRETTY** SILLY!

OH, YEAH, YOU'RE A **BRILLIANT** JUDGE!

NOW-- WHERE ARE WE GONNA FIND A **COW SUIT?**

WHAT? I GET TO WEAR A **COW** SUIT?! **COOL!** HAVE ANOTHER **BEER**, PARTNER!

KEEP IT **DOWN**, YOU CORN HEAD! I DON'T WANT ANYBODY TO KNOW WE'RE **TOGETHER**!

OH! RIGHT! GOTCHA!

OH, NO! NOT **ANOTHER** ONE!! YOU BETTER BE ABLE TO **PAY** FOR THOSE BEERS, SHORTY!

DON'T WORRY! I'LL PRETEND I DON'T KNOW YOU . . . HUM TE DUM

THAT'S **FIVE MUGS** OF MY **BEST ALE!** YOU OWE ME **TWO EGGS**, AN' I WANT IT **NOW!**

RELAX, KING KONG! I'M GOOD FOR IT!

DOO, DOO!

JUST LIKE THIS **OTHER** IDIOT WAS **GOOD** FOR IT?!

OH, MY! LOOK AT ALL THESE DIRTY GLASSES!

I'VE HAD IT UP TO **HERE** WITH YOU DRIFTERS COMIN' INTO TOWN FOR TH' FESTIVAL -- TRYIN' TO GET **BEER** ON **CREDIT!**

QUIT BREATHIN' IN MY **CUP!**

IT'S **MY** CUP UNTIL YOU PAY ME THE **TWO EGGS** YOU OWE ME!!

JEEZ! WHAT A **HOTHEAD!** HERE! TAKE IT!

WHAT'S THIS?

TWO **EGGS**, PAL! WHAT? DID TH' PRICE GO UP?

OKAY, SHORTY! **GET** IN TH' KITCHEN! YOU CAN **WORK** OFF YER BAR TAB...

WH--?

HEY!

NOBODY MUTILATES A **MINT NOTE** AROUND **ME** AN' LIVES TO **TELL** ABOUT IT! **SAY YER PRAYERS, CHUCKLES!**

THEY DON'T **USE** MONEY HERE, CUZ! THEY'VE NEVER EVEN **SEEN** IT BEFORE!

COME AGAIN?

THEY TRADE **GOODS** AND **SERVICES**. IT'S A **BARTER SYSTEM!**

CHUCKLES WANTS **REAL EGGS!**

YOUR BUTT IS **MINE,** BALDY!

SMILEY -- **WHY** DID YOU KEEP GIVING ME BEER? YOU **KNOW** I DON'T CARRY **DAIRY PRODUCTS!!**

UH, OH! LOOKS LIKE I MISSED SOME OF THOSE DIRTY GLASSES!

....DEFIANCE WILL NOT BE TOLERATED...... .....ONCE *WE* RETURN ORDER TO THE VALLEY......

STAY BACK!

SNIFF! SNIFF!

WAIT A MINUTE! WAIT A MINUTE!

DO YOU **SMELL** THAT?!

IT'S BRIMSTONE! IT'S THE **DRAGON**! HE'S **HERE**!

OH, NO.

RELAX, THORN! EVERYTHING'S GONNA BE **OKAY**!

FONE BONE! WHAT ARE YOU DOING?!

I KNOW **YOU** DON'T BELIEVE IN DRAGONS, BUT **THESE GUYS** DO! WATCH **THIS**!

OKAY, FELLAS! PARTY'S **OVER**! BREAK IT UP! **LET'S GO**! TH' DRAGON'LL BE HERE **ANY MINUTE** NOW, AN' YOU DON'T WANNA **BE** HERE WHEN HE SHOWS UP!

JUST THE **SIGHT** OF TH' DRAGON SENDS THESE GUYS INTO A **PANIC**! THEY RUN LIKE THEIR **FUR'S** ON FIRE!

ARE YOU **STILL** **HERE**? GO ON! **SHOO**!

I SMELL NOTHING...

WHAT ARE YOU **TALKIN'** ABOUT? YOU DON'T SMELL BRIMSTONE?

SSSSS

NO.

SNIFF! SNIFF! **THAT'S** WEIRD! I DON'T SMELL IT ANYMORE, EITHER!

LOOK OUT!

AARR

OOF!

CHUNK

WHY, LOOK, TED. IT'S A MEETING OF THE NEW COMMUNITY LEADERS.

OOH! A TOWN MEETING! DOES WE GITS TA VOTE? I JES LOVES TA VOTE!

HISSS! STAY BACK, WORM!

OUR NUMBERS ARE TOO GREAT!

EVEN FOR YOU!

FUNNY YOU SHOULD MENTION THAT-- HOW MANY WARRIORS DO YOU HAVE BETWEEN HERE AND THE WATERFALL? A THOUSAND? TWO THOUSAND?

HIYA, BONES! HEY, THORNY! C'MON OVER HERE!

SSSSS

I BELIEVE THIS VIOLATES OUR AGREEMENT...

YOU WOULD NOT BE SO BOLD IF KINGDOK WERE HERE!

YOU RUN AND TELL KINGDOK THAT I'M WATCHIN' HIM!

HE **DID** IT! **YES!** I **TOLD** YOU THERE WAS A DRAGON! I **TOLD** YOU!

MR. DRAGON . . .

MM?

. . . THE RAT CREATURES ATTACKED OUR FARM -- WE LEFT MY GRANDMOTHER THERE ALONE!

CLIMB ON MY BACK.

C'MON, FONE BONE!

OHMYGOSH

HOLD TIGHT!

HURRY!

...THEY MIGHT BE **WATCHING!**

I **DON'T** CARE **!!**

GRAN'MA!

I'LL GO **WITH** YA, THORNY! WAIT FOR **ME!**

C'MON!

GRAN'MA? CAN YOU HEAR ME?

GRAN'MA BEN! WHERE ARE YOU?

CRASH TINKLE!

THORN?
IS THAT
YOU, DEAR?

OH, GOOD!
YOU'RE SAFE!

CRUNCH!
TINK!

GRAN'MA--!

ARE YOU
ALL
RIGHT?

OF COURSE I AM, DEAR!
I FOUGHT TH' RATS BACK
IN TH' **BIG** WAR! BESIDES,
I WASN'T **REALLY** IN DANGER. . .

. . . WHEN YOU AN' **BONE** LEFT TH'
HOUSE, ALL TH' **FIGHT** WENT OUT
OF 'EM! I WAS **MUCH** MORE
WORRIED ABOUT **YOU**!

WE ALMOST GOT CAUGHT,
BUT THE **DRAGON** SAVED US!

A **REAL** DRAGON, GRAN'MA! **LOOK!**

I CAN SEE.

HELLO, DRAGON.

HELLO, ROSE. IT'S BEEN A WHILE.

YEP.

WELL... LOOKS LIKE EVERYTHING'S UNDER CONTROL HERE. GUESS I'LL BE GOIN'.

YEP.

C'MON, TED.

GRAN'MA! WHAT ARE YOU **DOING**?! THE DRAGON JUST SAVED OUR **LIVES**!

NOT NOW, THORN. MR. BONE FROM BONEVILLE AN' I HAVE TO HAVE A LITTLE **CHAT**!

AND **YOU** HAVE A LOT OF THINGS TO DO BEFORE WE LEAVE FOR TH' **SPRING FAIR!**

THE **FAIR**?! YOU'RE NOT STILL WORRIED ABOUT YOUR **COW RACE**?!

WHAT ABOUT **PHONEY BONE** AN' **SMILEY**? WE HAVE TO **FIND** THEM!

BONE AND I WILL HITCH UP TH' CART. **YOU** BE A SWEETHEART AND PUT OUT TH' **FIRE** ON TH' ROOF!

SHE'S NOT EVEN **LISTENING** TO US! CAN YOU **BELIEVE** SHE WANTS TO GO TO TH' FAIR?!

ARE YOU **KIDDING?** I STILL CAN'T GET OVER TH' FACT THAT SHE HAS A **FIRST NAME!**

DEAR . . . I'M NOT A **COMPLETE** NINCOMPOOP! WE'LL BE **SAFER** IN TOWN! **AND**, WITH ANY LUCK, WE'LL BE ABLE TO FIND HIS **COUSINS!**

BUT --

PLEASE, THORN! WE **HAVE** TO **GO!** WE DON'T KNOW IF THEY'RE **SAFE!**

YOU'RE RIGHT! I'LL TAKE CARE OF THE ROOF!

WE PACKED EVERYTHING LAST NIGHT, SO TH' LUGGAGE IS ALREADY OUT IN TH' BARN. COME JOIN US WHEN YOU GET DONE.

C'MON, BONE!

GRAN'MA? WHAT **WAS** THAT WITH YOU AN' TH' DRAGON? DO YOU GUYS **KNOW** EACH OTHER?

I'LL ASK TH' QUESTIONS! I WANNA KNOW WHY THOSE MONSTERS WERE AFTER **YOU** . . . AN' I WANT TH' **TRUTH!**

I HAVE **NO** IDEA! **HONEST!** I'VE NEVER DONE **ANYTHING** TO THEM!

WHAT ABOUT THAT SHIFTY **COUSIN** OF YOURS? YOU THINK **PHONEY BONE** MIGHT'VE HAD SOME DEALIN'S WITH 'EM?

NO, MA'M! WE DON'T **HAVE** RAT CREATURES BACK WHERE WE COME FROM!

IN FACT, WE NEVER EVEN **HEARD** OF RAT CREATURES BEFORE WE GOT RUN OUT OF BONEVILLE!

WELL, ACTUALLY, **I** WASN'T RUN OUTTA BONEVILLE -- **PHONEY** WAS! SMILEY AN' I JUST HELPED HIM GET AWAY!

WHAT'D HE **DO?**

PHONEY DECIDED HE WAS GONNA RUN FOR **MAYOR!** HIS CAMPAIGN SLOGAN WAS: "AN' I'VE GOT TH' MONEY TO **DO** IT, TOO!"

SO TH' BONES RAN HIM OUTTA TOWN FOR **THAT,** HUH? WELL, **GOOD** FOR THEM!

NO.

ANYBODY CAN RUN FOR MAYOR. EVEN **PHONEY!**

THAT GREEDY, LITTLE **LOUDMOUTH?** NOT IN **MY** TOWN HE COULDN'T!

WELL, HE CAN IN BONEVILLE. **ANYWAY,** HE WANTED TO MAKE THE **OFFICIAL** ANNOUNCEMENT A BIG **SOCIAL EVENT,** SO HE DECIDED TO THROW A PICNIC DOWN ON TH' BANKS OF TH' **ROLLING BONE** RIVER . . .

THERE'S A **BEAUTIFUL** PARK THERE WITH GREEN, SLOPING LAWNS THAT STRETCH TO THE EDGE OF TH' WATER. IT'S JUST FAR ENOUGH AWAY FROM TH' **HUSTLE** AN' **BUSTLE** OF DOWNTOWN BONEVILLE THAT THERE WOULDN'T BE ANY **DISTRACTIONS!**

PHONEY INVITED **EVERYBODY** IN TOWN - - AN' HE PROMISED **FREE FOOD** FOR ANYONE WHO SHOWED UP! PRETTY SOON, TH' **PICNIC** WAS TH' **TALK** OF **BONEVILLE!**

THEN TH' BIG DAY ARRIVED, AN' TH' **WHOLE TOWN** TURNED OUT! TH' KIDS WERE PLAYIN' UNDER TH' TREES, AN' THE WOMEN WORE SUNBONNETS AN' FANCY DRESSES! THE PICNIC WAS OFF TO A **PERFECT START!**

THERE'S A **STATUE** IN TH' PARK OF BONEVILLE'S **FOUNDER** - - "BIG" JOHNSON BONE - - AN' SINCE MY COUSINS AN' I ARE **DESCENDANTS** OF HIS, PHONEY WANTED TO MAKE HIS ANNOUNCEMENT IN FRONT OF TH' STATUE.

. . . AND JUST TO **ADD** TO TH' FESTIVITIES, PHONEY HAD A **50** ft. **BALLOON** MADE OF HIMSELF! TH' BALLOON WAS TIED TO OL' "BIG" JOHNSON!

FASTEN THAT END THERE, WOULD YOU, BONE?

EVERYTHING WAS GOIN' **GREAT!** FOLKS WERE LISTENIN' TO TH' **FIREHOUSE** BAND AN' ENJOYIN' TH' SUNSHINE! TH' FOOD WAS PASSED OUT AN' THERE WERE PLENTY OF **PRUNE TARTS** FOR **EVERYONE!**

PRUNE TARTS?

YEAH. YOU KNOW PHONEY. HE GOT A **GOOD DEAL** ON SOME PRUNES FROM A DISCOUNT **PRUNE BROKER!**

OF COURSE!

SO ANYWAY, HE MAKES THE **ANNOUNCEMENT**, RIGHT? HE GETS UP AND DECLARES HIS CANDIDACY FOR **MAYOR** OF **BONEVILLE!**

I STILL THINK **THAT'S** WHEN THEY SHOULD'VE RUN HIM OUT!

THAT'S WHEN A GUST OF WIND CAME OFF TH' RIVER AND PULLED TH' **BALLOON** LOOSE! THE STATUE CAME OFF ITS **BASE** AN' WAS DANGLIN' OFF TH' BALLOON'S **ANKLE!** ALL OF A **SUDDEN**, THIS GIANT, INFLATABLE PHONEY BONE STARTED MOVING TOWARD THE **CROWD!**

OH, MY!

YEAH, IT WAS **AMAZING!** MY FIRST-GRADE TEACHER, **MISS CRAB-BONE**, WAS THE FIRST TO **PANIC!** SHE STARTED SCREAMING AND RUNNING BACK AN' FORTH! THE BALLOON CHASED HER INTO TH' **RIVER** BEFORE SMILEY AND I COULD LET THE **AIR** OUT OF IT!

...IT WAS **AWFUL!** EVERYONE WAS **STUNNED!** AT FIRST NOBODY MOVED! THEY JUST **SAT** THERE WITH THIS LOOK OF **HORROR** ON THEIR FACES!

AN' **THAT'S** WHEN THEY RAN YOU OUTTA TOWN.

NO. THAT'S WHEN TH' **BAD PRUNES** KICKED IN...

...I JUST WANT YOU TO **KNOW**... I'VE BEEN **WORKING** ON **THE PLAN!** I BEEN SPREADIN' **RUMORS** ALL DAY THAT **GRAN'MA BEN** IS **TOO OLD** TO WIN TH' RACE THIS YEAR!

IS ANYBODY **BUYIN'** IT?

I'M TH' BARTENDER! THEY **GOTTA** BELIEVE ME!

THIS IS **TOO** EASY! WE'LL COVER ALL TH' BETS, AND THEN WHEN GRAN'MA **WINS**, WE'LL BE **RICH!**

OF COURSE, WHEN GRAN'MA GETS INTO **TOWN**, EVERYBODY'S GONNA **SEE** SHE'S PERFECTLY FIT!

I'VE GOT THAT COVERED WITH **PHASE TWO:** THE MYSTERY COW! A **COW** THAT WE'LL **BUILD UP** IN EVERYBODY'S IMAGINATION THAT **CAN'T BE BEAT!**

WAIT! IS **THAT** TH' PART WHERE I GET TO WEAR TH' **COW SUIT?!** OH, **JOY!**

YEAH, **THAT'S** TH' PART! BUT YOU'RE GONNA **THROW** TH' RACE! REMEMBER! WE WANT GRAN'MA BEN TO WIN!

WELL, **NATURALLY**, I'M LOOKING FORWARD TO WEARIN' A **COW SUIT** -- BUT WHAT DO **YOU** GET OUT OF IT? AFTER **ALL**, THE LOCALS DON'T USE **MONEY!** THEY TRADE **GOODS 'N' SERVICES!**

IT **DOES** SOUR MY PLANS FOR AMASSING A **HUGE** FORTUNE AND RETURNING TO BONEVILLE IN **TRIUMPH**... STILL, THE PLAY IS TH' THING!

IF ALL THESE YOKELS **HAVE** ARE **POULTRY PRODUCTS**, THEN I'LL TAKE IT!!

BESIDES, I HAVE A **HANKERIN'** TO TAKE TH' PROPRIETOR OF THIS FINE ESTABLISHMENT TO TH' **CLEANERS!** YOU **WITH** ME?

SURE! IT DOESN'T MAKE ANY DIFFERENCE TO ME! BUT THEN ... NOT MUCH **DOES!**

GOOD. NOW GET BACK OUT THERE AND KEEP SPREADIN' **RUMORS!**

AN' QUIT BRINGIN' ME DIRTY DISHES TO WASH!

PHONCIBLE P. BONE.....AT **LAST** I HAVE FOUND YOU.....

WHO, **ME?** HOW DO YOU KNOW MY NAME?

...YOU SHOULD BE GRATEFUL INDEED THAT YOUR FRIENDS INTERFERED ON YOUR BEHALF LAST NIGHT.... I AM FORCED TO USE MUCH MORE SUBTLE METHODS OF CONTACTING YOU....

WHAT TH' **HECK** ARE YOU **TALKIN'** ABOUT?

.... YOUR COUSIN FONE BONE HAS AWAKENED THE GREAT RED DRAGON..... ... FOR THIS ... ... I WILL **KILL** HIM .....

SORRY, CUZ, BUT LUCIUS SAYS YOU GOTTA WASH THESE!

UH, OH.

...SO THERE HE IS, OKAY? **ISHMAEL'S** LAYIN' IN HIS BUNK WAITIN' FOR HIS MYSTERIOUS NEW ROOMMATE TO SHOW UP ... **SUDDENLY** -- AT LIKE, **3 O' CLOCK** IN TH' MORNING -- TH' DOOR SWINGS **OPEN** ... AN' THERE, STANDIN' IN TH' DOORWAY, WITH TH' LIGHT FROM TH' HALL BEHIND HIM, IS **QUEEQUEG!** AN' HE'S **CARRYIN' SHRUNKEN HEADS !!**

WHAT'S GOING ON, BACK THERE?

OH ... H'LO, THORN.

ARE YOU TALKING ABOUT **MOBY DICK** **AGAIN?**

IT JUST SO HAPPENS THAT GRAN'MA **LIKES** TO HEAR ABOUT **GOOD BOOKS!** SHE **APPRECIATES** FINE LITERATURE!

HEY, GRAN'MA! WAKE UP!

ZZ--SNORT!

WHA -- ARE WE THERE ALREADY?

DOO-OOP!

NOT QUITE. BUT I THOUGHT I SHOULD WAKE YOU UP.

IS SOMETHING WRONG?

IT LOOKS LIKE THE ROAD IS BLOCKED UP AHEAD. THERE ARE SOME TREES DOWN ACROSS THE PATH.

STOP TH' COWS.

HMM.

THERE'S A MAN STANDING UNDER THE TREES JUST OFF TO THE SIDE OF THE ROAD. YOU SEE THAT?

WELL, I'LL **BE!** THAT LOOKS LIKE LITTLE JONATHAN OAKS! LET'S FIND OUT WHAT HE'S **UP** TO! ☀KIK☀ ☀KIK☀ LET'S GO, COW!

GOOD AFTERNOON, JON OAKS!

WHAT IN TH' **WORLD** ARE YOU **DOIN'?** WHY ARE THESE TREES BLOCKIN' TH' **ROAD?**

GOOD DAY, GRAN'MA BEN! **LUCIUS** HAD US BLOCK TH' ROAD! THERE WAS SOME STRANGE DOIN'S IN TH' **WOODS** LAST NIGHT. TH' **HAIRY MEN** WERE OUT!

OF **COURSE** WE STUCK TOGETHER! WE'RE **FRIENDS**, AREN'T WE?

HURRY UP, NOW, KIDS! WE'RE HERE!

About JEFF SMITH

JEFF SMITH was born and raised in the American Midwest. He learned about cartooning from comic strips, comic books, and watching animated shorts on TV. After four years of drawing comic strips for Ohio State University's student newspaper and cofounding Character Builders animation studio in 1986, Smith launched the comic book *BONE* in 1991. Between *BONE* and other comics projects, Smith spends much of his time on the international guest circuit promoting comics and the art of graphic novels.

More about *BONE*

Instant classics when they first appeared in the U.S. as underground comic books in 1991, the *BONE* books have since garnered 38 international awards and sold a million copies in 15 languages. Now, Scholastic's **GRAPHIX** imprint is publishing full-color graphic novel editions of the nine-book *BONE* series. Look for the continuing adventures of the Bone cousins in *The Great Cow Race.*